Can You Find It Unicorn World

A Cute Magical I Spy Book for Toddlers and Preschool Kids with Unicorns, Fairies, Rainbows, and Fantasy Hidden Objects

Can you find 3 fluffy pink clouds?

Can you find 2 sparkling red mushrooms?

Can you find 1 golden key?

Can you find 3 blue magical pebbles?

Can you find 4 yummy-looking cupcakes?

Can you find 5 glowing yellow stars?

Can you find 2 silver crowns?

Can you find 3 large purple diamonds?

Can you find 1 ancient spellbook?

Can you find all the unicorns hiding in the scene?

Can you find 2 hot air balloons?

Can you find 3 little owls?

Can you find 4 pink lotus flowers?

Can you find 5 lollipops?

Can you find 2 pirate hats?

Can you find 3 orange starfish?

Can you find 1 red dragon egg?

Can you find 4 yellow balloons?

Can you find 2 heart-shaped cookies?

Can you find all the hidden unicorns?

The Floating Islands
Can you find 2 purple butterflies?
21

The Bubble Garden

Can you find 3 blue bubbles?

The Enchanted Treehouse

Can you find 1 lantern? 

The Rainbow River

Can you find 4 yellow ducks?

The Ice Crystal Cave

Can you find 2 snowflakes?

The Treasure Lagoon

Can you find 3 red starfish?

The Music Meadow

Can you find 2 music notes? ♫ ♫

The Crystal Waterfall

Can you find 3 green gems?

Unicorn Tea Party

Can you find 2 teacups?

The Grand Unicorn Parade
Can you find 5 balloons?
30

Made in the USA
Monee, IL
05 November 2026

67382337R00019